Parents' Magazine Press

Simply Fun!
Things to Make and Do
by James Razzi
Edited by Patricia Kienzle

To Signe and Christina

Printed in the United States of America
Library of Congress Catalog Card Number: 68-11660

CONTENTS

INTRODUCTION

Simply Fun is more than a keep-busy book. Using simple cut-and-paste methods, a child may learn to better grasp such concepts as size, shape, color and texture, not to mention simple mechanics. He may propel a pop-stick boat or make operative a heat-and-air toy. And all the while, many necessary manual skills, such as eye-hand coordination, are being more fully developed.

Each activity is explained in easy-to-follow terms with numbered illustration figures for added visual clarity. But no cutting, please! **Simply Fun** is a book-shelf book, to be passed down through a line of active youngsters and used over and over again. And there's no need for exotic hobby materials. A few sheets of construction paper, a jar of paste or a tube of glue, an assortment of buttons, yarns, paper clips and such household items, plus a pair of scissors, will handle all the activities nicely.

Learning can be especially fun when the experience is backed by creative motivation. Should a child be enthusiastic about construction, then he's encouraged to assemble a miniature town. For the aspiring scientist, a play microscope's just the thing, and a bright young musician can strum an oatmeal-box guitar. Excited youngsters will find many things to do alone, leaving the adult with little more to do than be an admiring audience!

Patricia Kienzle
Managing Editor
Humpty Dumpty's Magazine

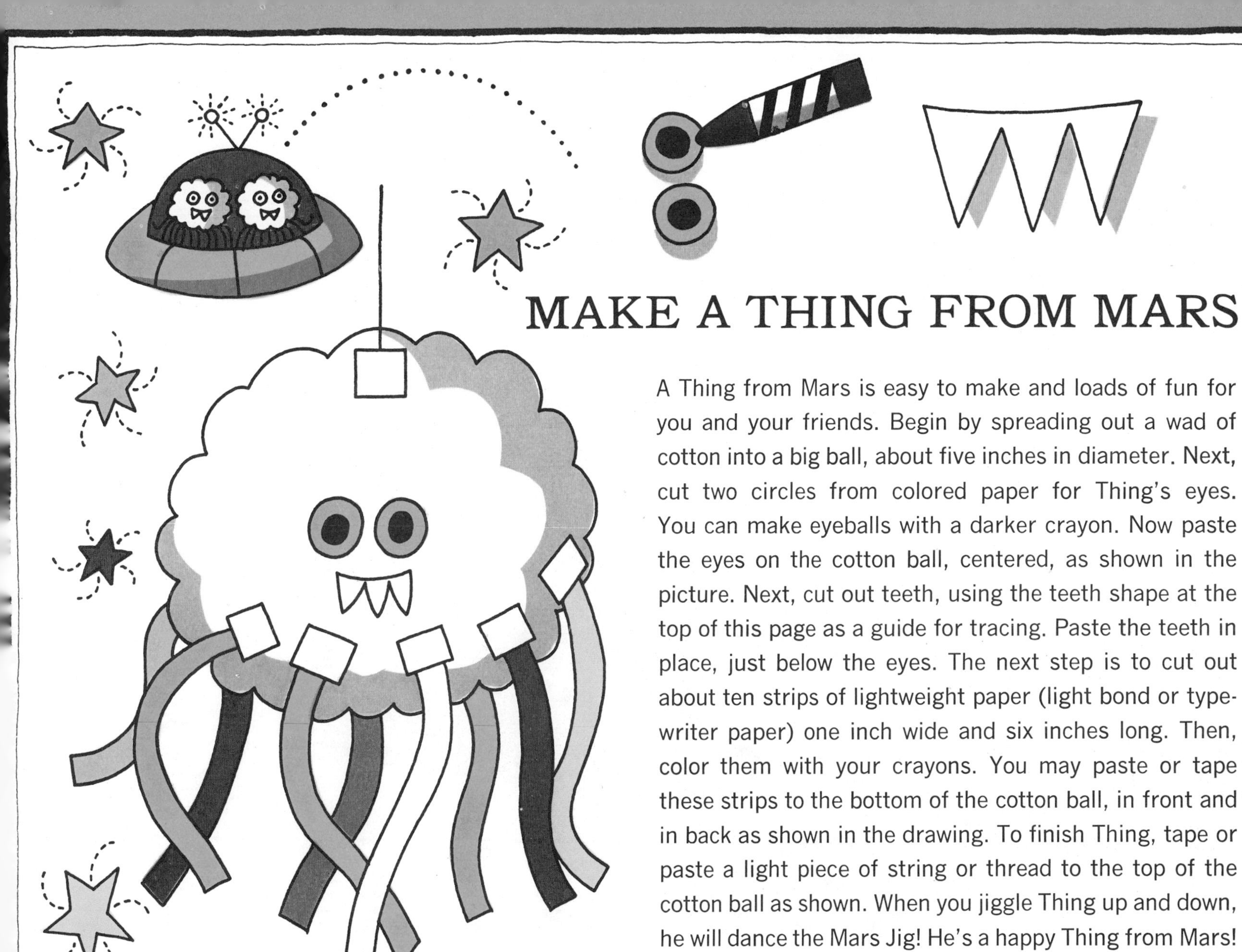

MAKE A THING FROM MARS

A Thing from Mars is easy to make and loads of fun for you and your friends. Begin by spreading out a wad of cotton into a big ball, about five inches in diameter. Next, cut two circles from colored paper for Thing's eyes. You can make eyeballs with a darker crayon. Now paste the eyes on the cotton ball, centered, as shown in the picture. Next, cut out teeth, using the teeth shape at the top of this page as a guide for tracing. Paste the teeth in place, just below the eyes. The next step is to cut out about ten strips of lightweight paper (light bond or type-writer paper) one inch wide and six inches long. Then, color them with your crayons. You may paste or tape these strips to the bottom of the cotton ball, in front and in back as shown in the drawing. To finish Thing, tape or paste a light piece of string or thread to the top of the cotton ball as shown. When you jiggle Thing up and down, he will dance the Mars Jig! He's a happy Thing from Mars!

AN OUTSTANDINGLY ORANGE LION!

Some very special lions can change color with just a bit of help from you. This lion may look blue now, but stare at the white dot on his mane for about 50 seconds. Then close your eyes tightly and turn toward a source of light while keeping your eyes closed. Soon you should see an Outstandingly Orange Lion. It's a bit of eye magic!

COLOR CHANGES

Make your own eye magic! Use any color crayon except black — red or green would be a good choice. Using a four-inch-square area, draw a bird, a star, a circle or anything else you wish. After you have completely colored in the figure, put a black dot in the center of your drawing. Stare at the black dot in the same way you stared at the Outstandingly Orange Lion. What color changes do you see for yourself with this eye magic?

PUT TWEETIE IN A CAGE

Eye tricks can be just as much fun as eye magic! For this trick you'll need a piece of white paper, three inches square. Construction paper is ideal. Draw a bird cage on one side of the paper square as shown in figure 1, filling up as much space as possible. (Just lines for bars drawn up and down on the paper can serve as a fine cage, too!) Now, turn the cage upside down. Then turn the paper square over and draw a bird on the other side. Maybe you'd like a canary, maybe a parrot, or even a sparrow! This is shown for you in figure 2.

1.

2.

The next step is taping two small pieces of string at the sides of the paper in the center of each side, as shown in figure 3.

Now, hold each string with your thumb and first finger as the boy in the picture is doing. Using your fingers, twirl the string so that the paper will twirl around also. You should see your own Tweetie safe and sound in the cage you drew just for him. Show this eye trick to all your friends!

THE MAGICAL ANSWER BOX

What will the Magical Answer Box have to say? Make your own and find out what is in the future as the box answers any yes-or-no question you choose to ask it.

Ask Mother for an empty oatmeal box, or any other similar type box which has a top. Paste strips of colorful construction paper around the box, making magic-like designs for your answer box. You may wish to decorate the top with paper stars or cutout designs. Next, cut a plain piece of cardboard about two inches square, and print YES on one side and NO on the other. Drop this cardboard into the box and put on the top. Ask the box any question which can be answered by either a YES or a NO. Shake up the Magical Answer Box, chanting some magic words as you shake. When you look deep in the box, you will see the answer to your question. Let your family and friends ask questions of the Magical Answer Box, too. It always has something to say!

THE PRETTY BUTTERFLY

Butterflies are colorful and graceful as they wing through the spring breeze. Now you can make your own lovely butterfly to wing about. Begin by folding a sheet of typewriter paper in half as shown in figure 1. Along the folded bottom, measure off about two inches on each side and mark this. From these marked points, cut the paper at an angle, working toward the end of the top corners as shown in figure 2. Next, measure about one inch up from the bottom fold. Fold down the sides from that one-inch point as shown in figure 3. You have just formed the butterfly's wings. Now cut out two small triangles from each wing, being sure to cut at the same place on each side as shown in figure 4. On to the next page for the completion of your butterfly!

1.

2.

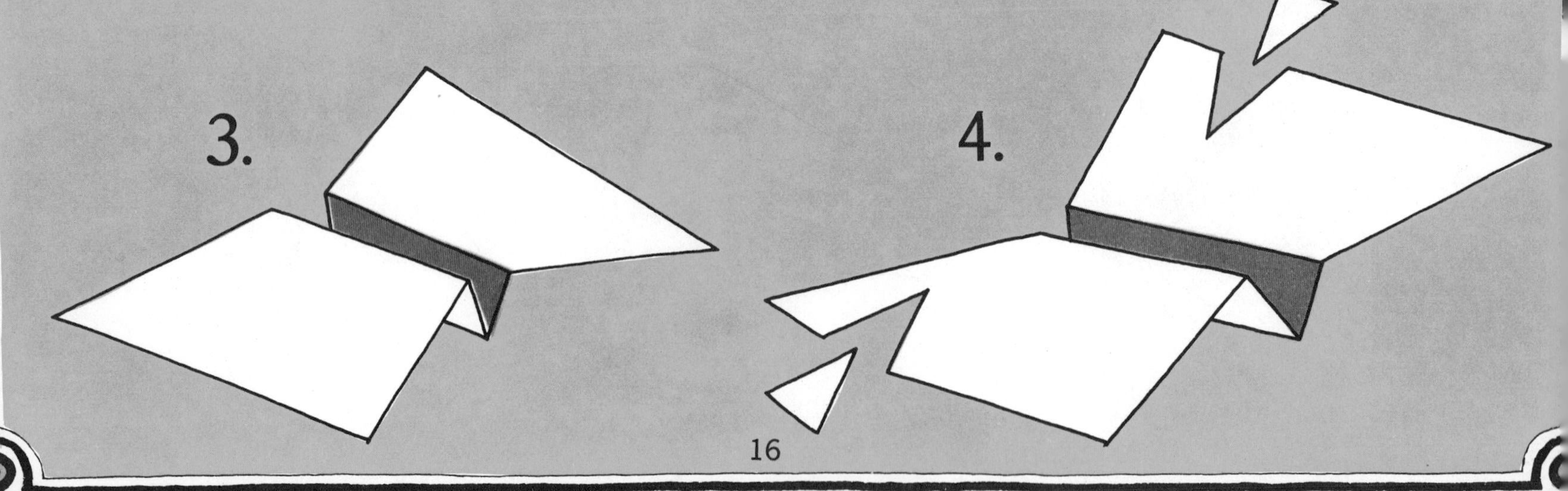

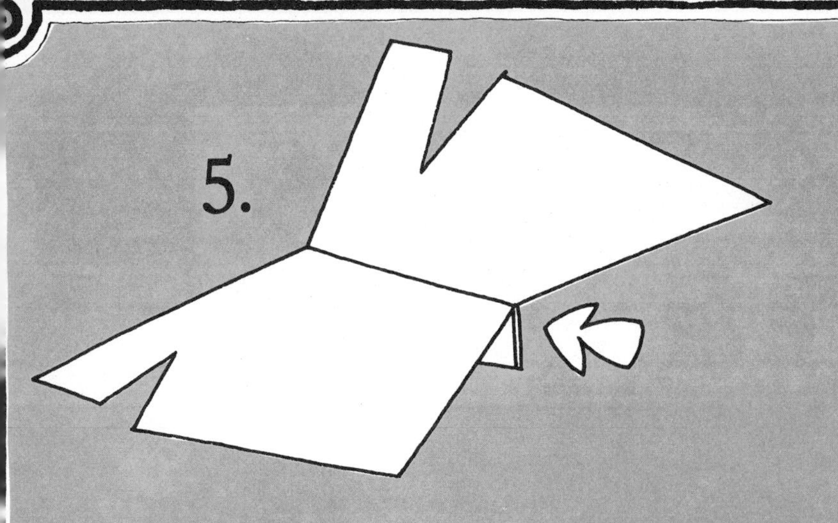

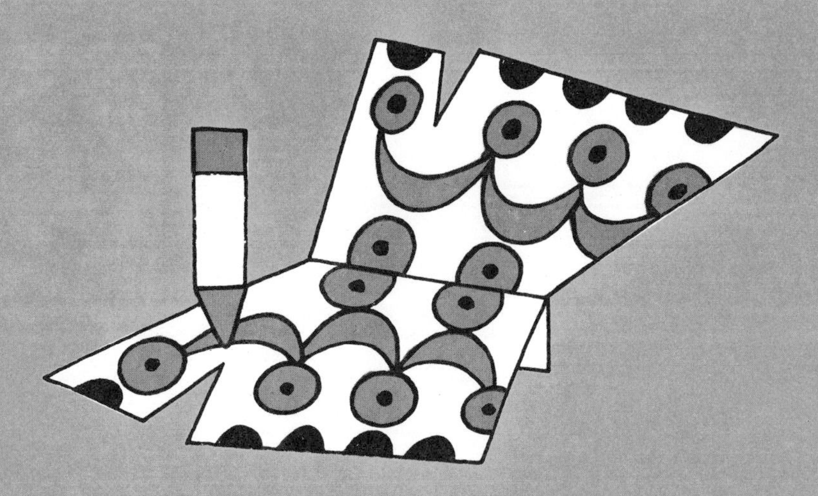

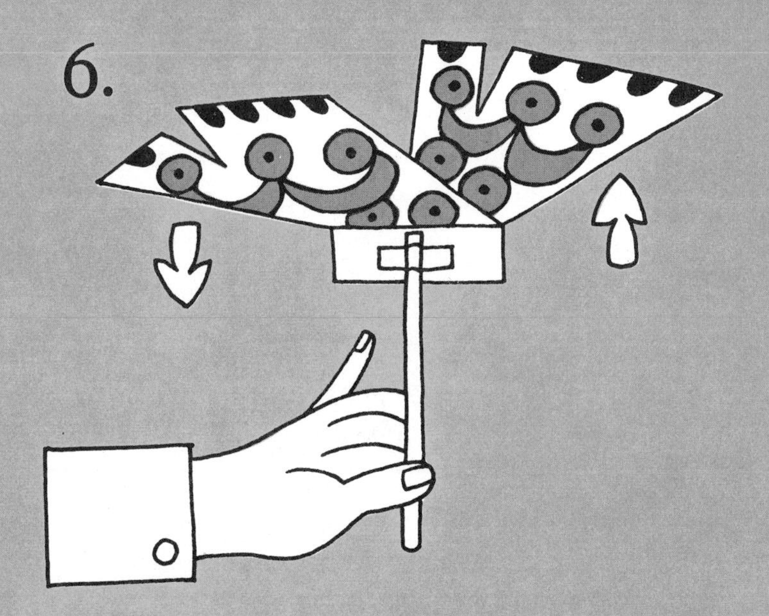

The next step is to paste together the folded area at the bottom as shown in figure 5. After the paste has dried, your butterfly is ready to be crayoned or water-colored in any design you choose. Perhaps you'd like to look at pictures or collections of butterflies to gather ideas for real butterfly designs. The last step is to tape one end of a straw or pencil to the bottom of the butterfly as shown in figure 6. When you move the straw (or pencil) up and down, your butterfly will flap its wings gracefully as you glide it through the air.

1.

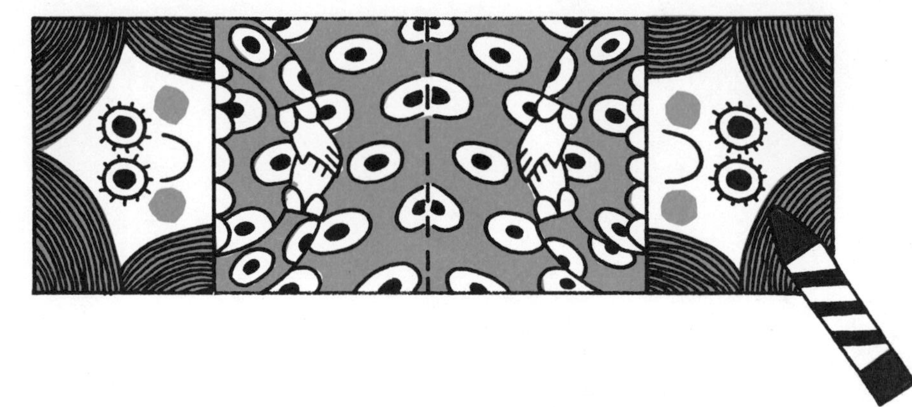

THE SAD-GLAD DOLLIE

Now you can make a dollie who's sad enough to cry one minute and glad enough to dance the next! She's a special sad-glad doll, an easy-to-make toy. To begin, cut out a strip of light-colored construction paper, approximately two inches wide and six inches long. Now, measure off three inches (this will be the center) and draw a dotted line there as shown in figure 1. Through the center of each half, draw a solid line as is shown in the same figure 1. The next step in making your dollie is to draw a very glad face on one end. On the other end of the strip, draw a very sad face. See figure 2. A suggestion: to draw the mouth for the glad side, draw a line like the U of the alphabet. For the sad side, draw a line like an upside-down U. Now on to the next page for final instructions.

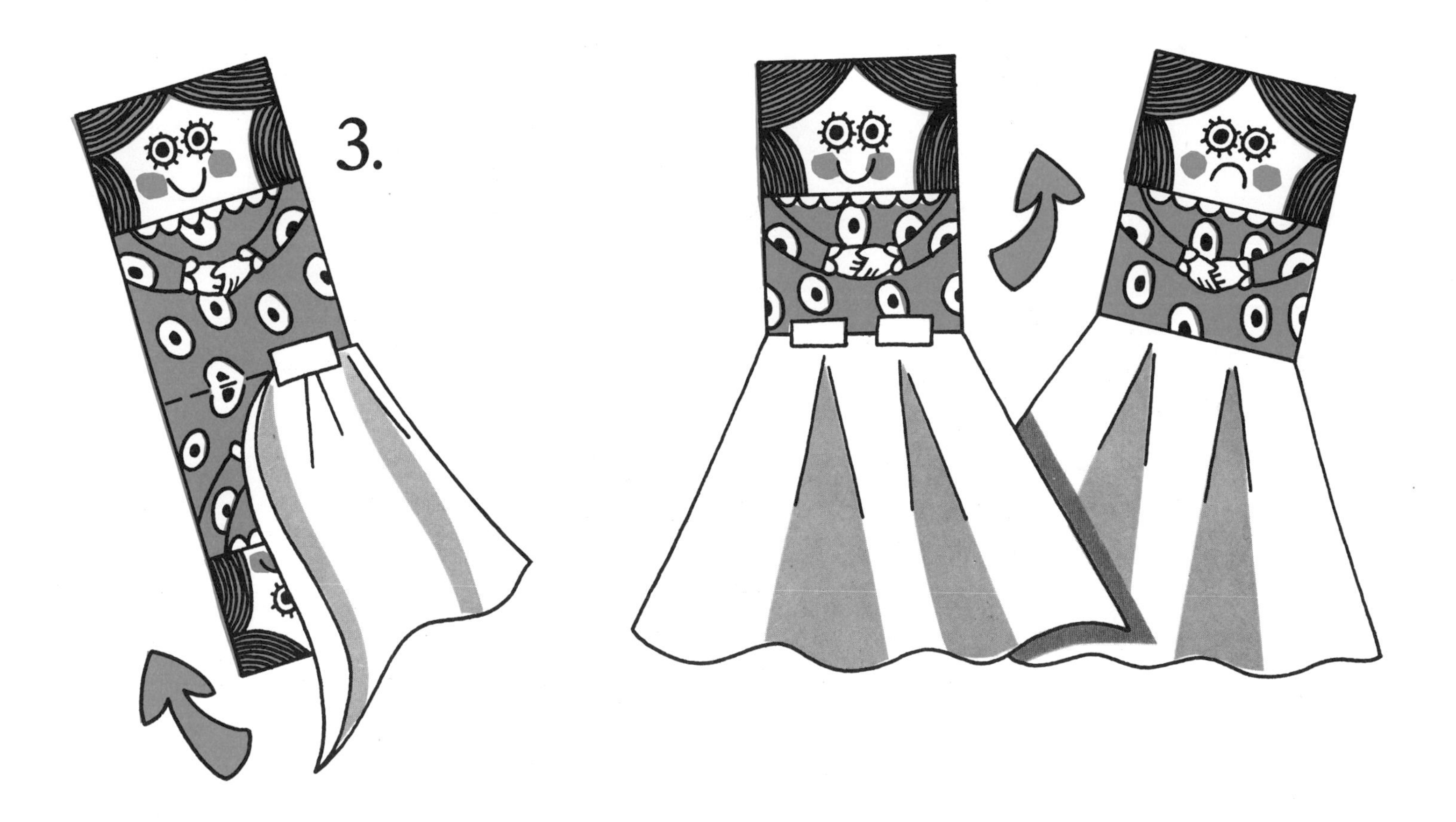

Tape one of the longer sides of a tissue to the dotted line marked in the center as shown in figure 3. The tissue should be carefully pleated along this line, forming a skirt. When you turn the dollie upside down, the tissue skirt should fall to the opposite side, revealing the other face of your dollie. One minute you can show a sad dollie — but with a turn and flip of the tissue, your dollie is glad again!

THE TWIRLY PROPELLER

Everyone shouts, "Good luck!" as the pilot waves. To see the plane's propeller turn round and round, just move this book in small circular motions, holding it about ten inches from your eyes. He's up, up and away!

THE FLIP-FLAP BUG

Your own Flip-Flap Bug can fill your bag of tricks with lots of excitement and surprises. First cut two rectangular shapes, 4½″ x 3″, from bond paper. Crayon or paint designs on each piece. Then roll each one tightly, the long way as shown in figure 1. Bend each in half as in figure 2. With a small rubber band, connect the two pieces together at the center bends as in figures 3 and 4. Twist the pieces in opposite directions until the rubber band feels tight. Now without letting it unwind, slip the Flip-Flap Bug under an upside-down cup. When some-one lifts the cup unsuspectingly, watch the Flip-Flap go!

A PAPER BAG ELEPHANT

Your own toy elephant (or one you might like to make as a gift) can be made with just a few simple materials found around the house. To begin, you'll need a medium-size grocery bag. Fill the lower half of the bag with rag scraps or crumpled newspaper until firm. Secure the elephant's body with string as shown in figure 1. The next step is to twist the unstuffed front half of the bag, as shown in figure 2, and secure it near the end of the elephant's trunk with string, also. Now your elephant is ready for two paper ears, cut like the shapes shown in figure 3, and four wooden clothespin legs. Paste on the ears and clip the clothespins to the bag as shown in figure 4. Now give your elephant paper circle eyes and a bit of cord for a tail. Why, he's ready for feeding time at your own private zoo!

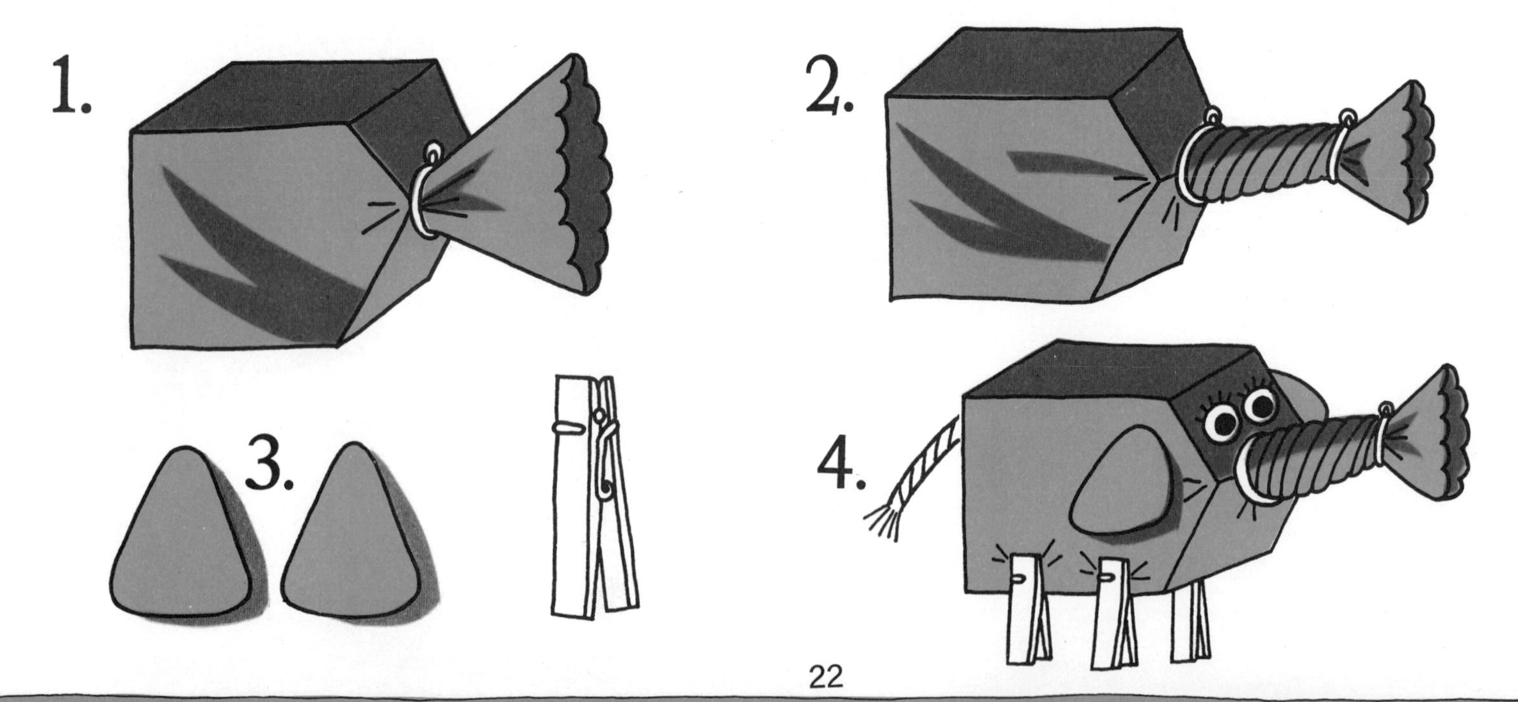

That's right — you can make a pair of earrings for yourself or for your mother. Begin by cutting two pieces of string, each about four inches long. Then tape a penny or a button or even a small pebble to each end of the string as shown in the picture. Do this for each earring. Now loop the strings over your ears. As you move your head, the earrings will make wonderful tingling, jingling sounds!

MAKE JINGLE-JANGLE EARRINGS

THE HEAT-AND-AIR TWIRLY

The Twirly twists and spirals in the breeze, near a source of heat or hanging in any airy spot. Sometimes it turns round and round — sometimes it moves only slightly. To make your Twirly, cut a circle from bond paper, about four inches in diameter. (A saucer or round box top placed on the paper as a guide will help you to draw, then cut, a perfect circle.) Place a dot in the center of this circle. Now, cut your circle in a spiral as shown by the dotted line in figure 1, following round and round, stopping near the dot. With a bit of cellophane tape, secure one end of a piece of thread to the dot as in figure 2.

To make your Twirly spin, grasp it by the end of the thread as the boy in the picture is doing. Hold Twirly over any source of heat or air, like a radiator or near an open window, and it will spin round and round without any help from you!

For extra fun with Twirly, wave it back and forth as the girl is doing. It will spin around in the air. Twirly can do many things and can even be hung by its thread like a mobile.

THE FLOATING-HEAD TRICK

Merlin is doing his famous Floating-Head Trick. To see his head float back to his body, stare at the black dot while bringing the page all the way up to your face until it touches your nose. Did you see the famous trick? It's a special kind of magic!

HAPPY OR SAD?

What makes Bobo the Clown happy? What makes Bobo sad? It's easy to find out. Place the straight edge of a piece of paper over the right side of Bobo's face, along the center line. Why is Bobo happy? Now, do the same thing on the other side of the clown's face. Can you see what has made Bobo sad?

YOUR OWN PENGUIN!

Rain or snow, ice or sun, your own penguin can be an all-season toy and loads of fun!

To start your paper penguin, cut a piece of white construction paper about four inches square and fold up one corner. Using a black crayon, color the paper as shown in figure 1.

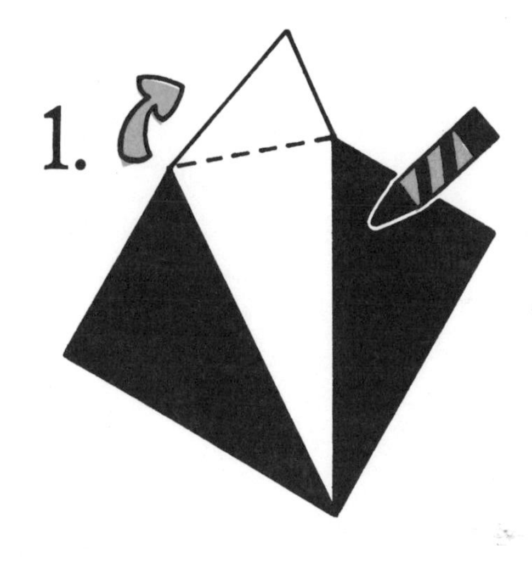

Next, on the reverse side of the folded corner, draw two eyes and a beak as shown in figure 2. Then fold back a small corner on the bottom as shown by the dotted line in the same figure.

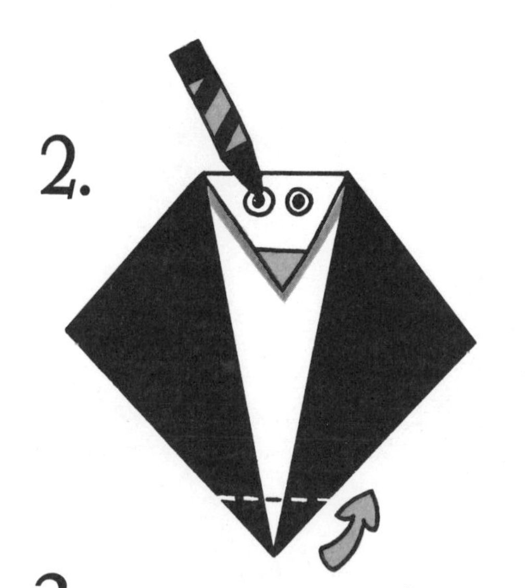

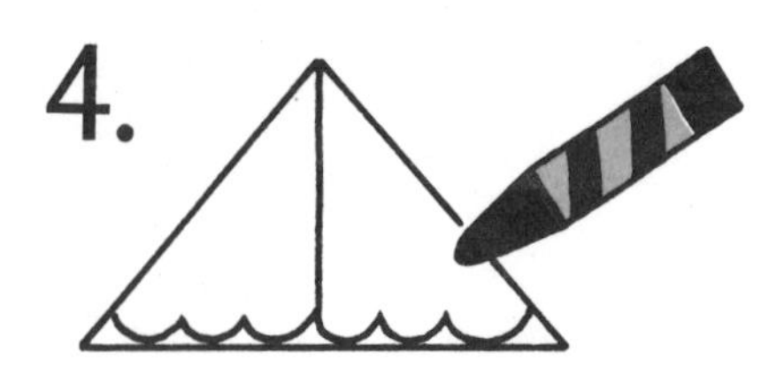

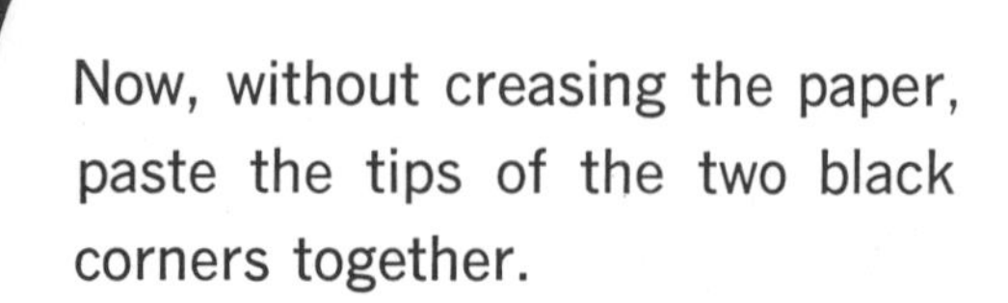

Now, without creasing the paper, paste the tips of the two black corners together.

To make feet, cut a small triangle of equal two-inch sides from white paper. Color the triangle yellow and draw feet and webbing as shown above. On to the next page for the finish!

The last step is to paste the folded bottom onto the center of the "feet" triangle. Your finished penguin should look like the boy's shown in this picture.

PAPER FLOWERS

Colorful paper flowers can brighten up your own room or your classroom. And since they are easy and fun to make, why not start a flower collection right away? Begin by cutting out strips of colored construction paper, approximately one inch by seven inches. One by one, tape the strips onto a large drinking straw, forming your flower petals. For an added touch, you may wish to paint the straw (the stem) green and sprinkle some perfume on the petals. Paper flowers are wonderful gifts for someone's birthday or for a special day like Mother's Day.

A WALKING FACE

No one has ever heard of a walking face, but now you can make one to show to your friends. To make this walking face, you will need a rectangular piece of colored construction paper. Draw the eyes and nose any way you wish. Now, cut out a rectangular mouth, large enough to slip four of your fingers through comfortably. When the walking face wants to take a stroll, just slip your fingers through the opening as shown below and take it out to meet the world!

STRUM AN OATMEAL-BOX GUITAR

Join the music fun with your homemade oatmeal-box guitar! The first step is to ask an adult to help you cut an empty oatmeal box in half. (Use the bottom half for your guitar.) With a nail file, make three notches in the open end. Directly across from these notches, make three more notches as shown below in figure 1. Now stretch three rubber bands across the top of the box and around the bottom, resting them in the notches as shown in figure 2. The most effective rubber bands should be half the length of the box's side when held lengthwise without any stretching. To make certain the bands stay in place, tape them on both sides. Now your musical instrument is ready to be strummed and you can be the first one in your neighborhood with an oatmeal-box guitar!

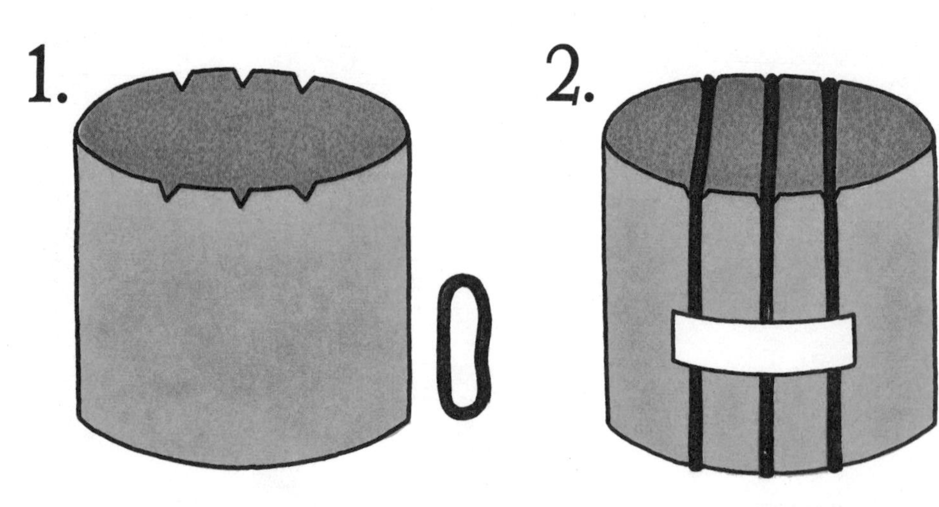

THE PADDLE BOAT

It's fun in the tub! It's fun in the sink! It's fun in a bowl! It's your speedy paddle boat! All you need in the way of materials are five ice pop sticks, all-purpose waterproof glue and a light rubber band. First, glue four ice pop sticks together as shown in figure 1. Allow the glue to dry thoroughly. It's a good idea to let it dry overnight. Your paddle is cut from half of another ice pop stick, following the sample shown in figure 2. Ask an adult to help you with this step since wood is difficult to cut. The adult should also notch the paddle and the lower part of the boat for you as shown by arrows. Now you can take over again by stretching a rubber band over the lower end of the boat, resting it in the notches there. Now slip in the paddle as shown and turn it in the direction shown by dotted arrows until it feels taut. Holding the paddle so that it does not unwind, place your paddle boat in water, making the paddle face the direction you want it to go. Release the paddle and just watch the speedy paddle boat make waves!

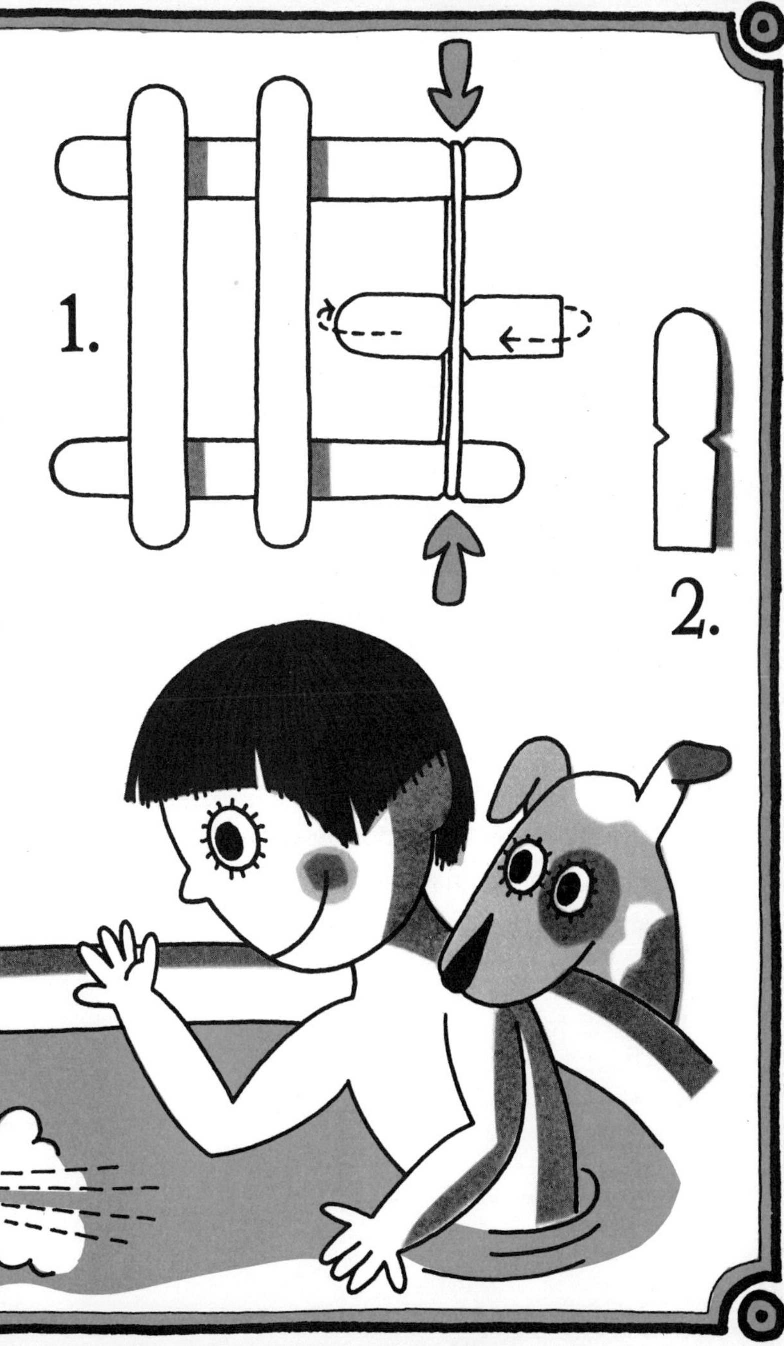

THE KING'S JESTER

The King's jester is a funny, scatter-brained clown who makes everyone laugh! To make a jester just like the King's you'll need a medium-size paper bag. Put a handful of rice in this bag along with enough crumpled-up newspaper to fill the jester's head. (Be sure the rice can still rattle around inside when bag is stuffed.) Next you'll need a cardboard tube such as the kind found inside a roll of kitchen foil or cellophane wrap. Put a sheet of crumpled-up newspaper in one end of the tube and insert this same end into the bag. This way, the rice won't fall out. To secure this tube tie a piece of string around the neck of the bag as shown in figure 2. Now draw the jester's happy face with crayons and cut the bottom of the bag into strips to make his collar. This is shown in figure 3. And for the top of your jester's head — paste approximately five straws together as shown in figure 4. If you press the straws flat in the center they will be easier to paste together and easier to paste on top of the jester's head. When all the paste has dried, your own jester is ready to put on a show in his rattly way!

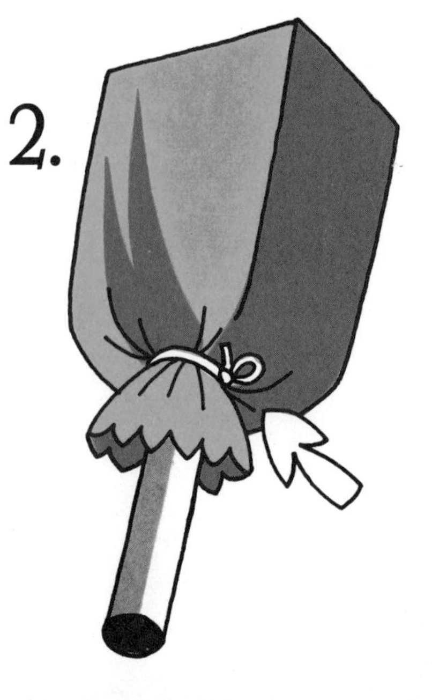

3.

4.

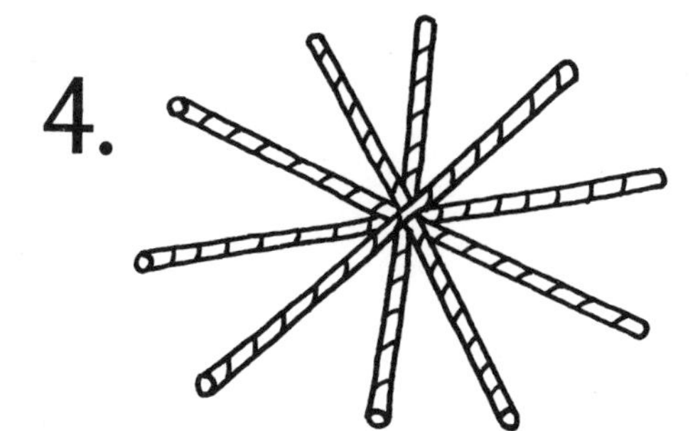

AN ODDS-AND-ENDS CHARM BRACELET

A colorful button, an old key, a bottle cap, a tiny pencil, a piece of macaroni — things from the kitchen, things from the workshop, things from a junk box — all these can be handy dandy odds and ends for your own special charm bracelet. Just make a paper clip chain to fit around your wrist like a bracelet. Then, tie on the odds-and-ends charms with colorful yarn or string. Slip the finished bracelet over your wrist and you're all set to show it off!

A profile is the outline of the side of someone's face. With just a piece of string you can give Mr. Change many different and funny profiles. First, cut a small piece of heavy string or yarn six inches long. Now, arrange it on the unfinished side of the face on this page so that it makes a nose and chin. You can change the nose and chin each time you want to make a different profile. Mr. Change can look like many different people.

CHANGE MR. CHANGE

MAKE A PUSSY CAT MASK

For Halloween or just for fun, make a pussy cat mask! First, choose a paper grocery bag that will fit comfortably over your head. On top of the bag, draw two triangles as shown by the example in figure 1, with the solid lines in the front. Cut along the dotted lines of your triangles only, and fold the "ears" forward on the solid lines. Then cut two round holes on one side for eyes as shown in the drawing. Now draw the nose and mouth. For whiskers, cut out four thin strips from lightweight paper and paste two on each side of the pussy cat's mouth. How many people will guess your true identity when you're wearing this pussy cat mask?

MAKE A TWIRLY SNAKE

It's a snake to make to wiggle and twirl. Begin by cutting out a strip of light bond paper, approximately one inch by eight inches. Now draw a snake-like design on the strip. At one end, make two black dots for eyes. Then tape the tail of the snake near the lower end of a long pencil as shown in the drawing to the right. For the next step you will need a piece of string about six inches long. Tape one end of this string to the top of the pencil, near the tip. Now tape a paper clip (or a small button) and the other end of the string to the back of the snake's head. Your snake is now ready to twirl. Hold the lower part of the pencil and twirl it around with your fingers. You can take this snake around to show everyone — he's a very safe type!

LET'S MAKE A TOWN!

Become the builder of your own town! Plan it, make it, set it up! To begin, fold a sheet of construction paper into three equal parts, folding in from the shorter sides as shown in figure 1. The roof-like effect is made by cutting away a small section of the sides at the top as shown in figure 2. You can decide on any "style" you like for the remaining roof section. Perhaps the pictures below will help you with this step. Your building now needs doors and windows and any other decorations you wish to draw with crayons or paint. When one building is complete, on to the next — maybe a house, maybe a store, maybe the Town Hall! If you'd like cars in your town, fold small rectangular-shaped pieces of construction paper into three parts as shown in figure 3. Then draw on wheels and the car body design. Your town can grow and grow, whenever you wish!

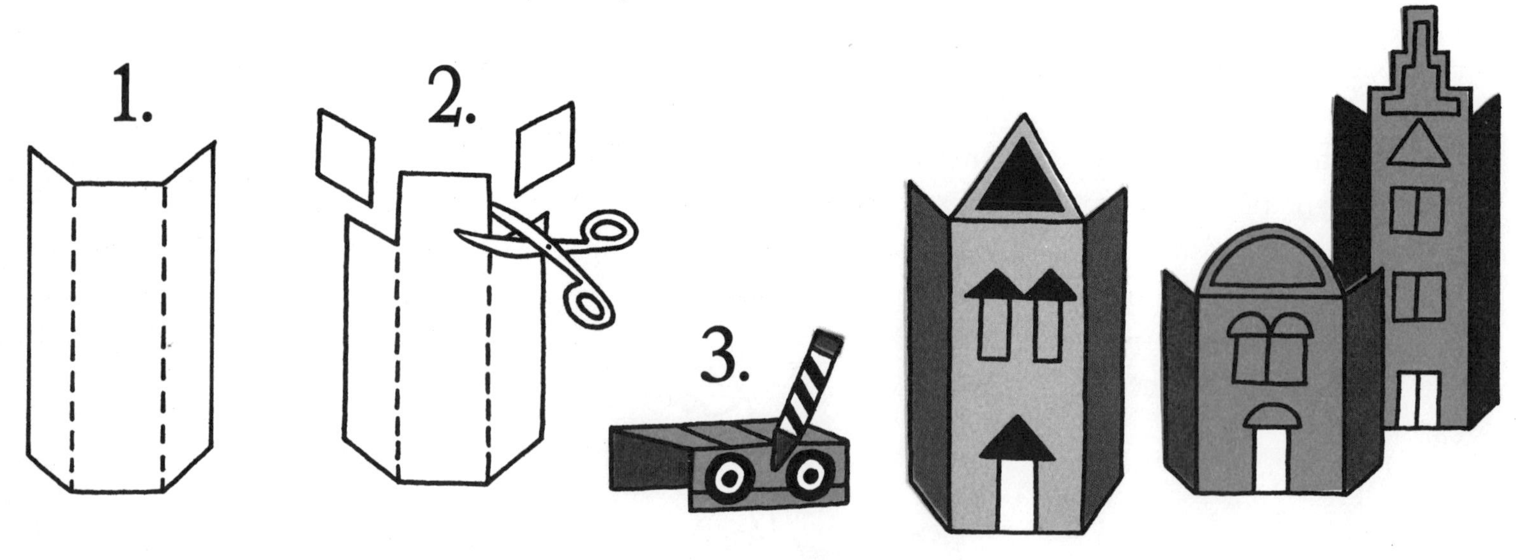

ROPE 'EM COWBOY!

Every rootin' tootin' cowboy needs his own special lasso. To make yours, begin by rolling up a few sheets of newspaper tightly, the long way. Next, tie the ends together with string, forming a circle. Now tie a length of heavy cord onto the newspaper circle. With some practice you can rope 'em all!

WATERCOLOR WHIMSIES

Each time you try, your Watercolor Whimsy will be different. Sometimes funny, sometimes pretty, sometimes mysterious! No two Whimsies can be alike. To create each Whimsy, dip a brush into watercolor paint so that it is watery and will drip off the brush easily, onto the paper. Now drip two or even three different colors onto a sheet of white paper. Working quickly, before the paint begins to dry, fold the paper in half, painted side in. Next, rub up and down on the folded paper several times. When you open up the folded paper, your surprise Whimsy is ready for display. Black ink in place of paint will create some interesting shadow Whimsies for you. What will your designs look like?

SOUTH SEA NECKLACE

Whether you make your South Sea Necklace as part of a masquerade costume or for dress-up, not only will it be fun to make, but also fun to wear! First, cut ten circles, approximately three inches in diameter, from different colors of construction paper. Make a small hole in the center of each circle for string or yarn to pass through as shown in figure 1. Next, from your colorful construction paper, cut ten squares, each measuring 3½" x 3½". Roll tubes from these squares and secure them with bits of cellophane tape as shown in figure 2. Now begin stringing the shapes onto a piece of string or yarn, alternating circles and tubes, until your necklace is finished and ready to tie on.

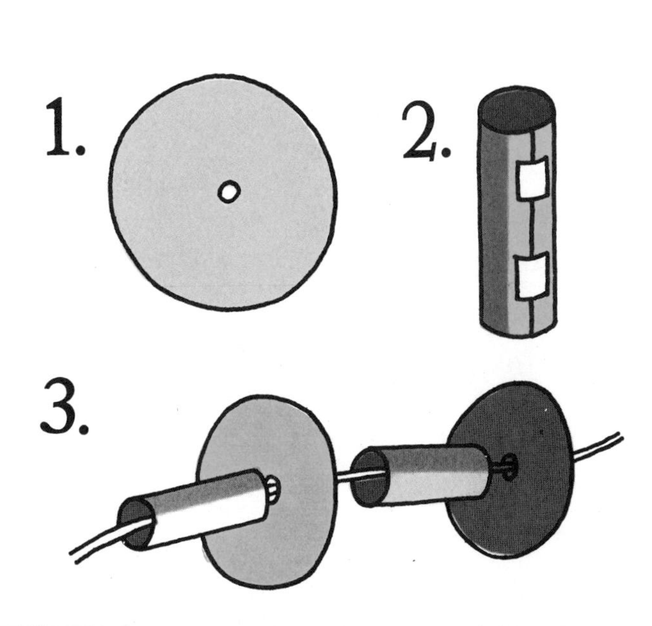

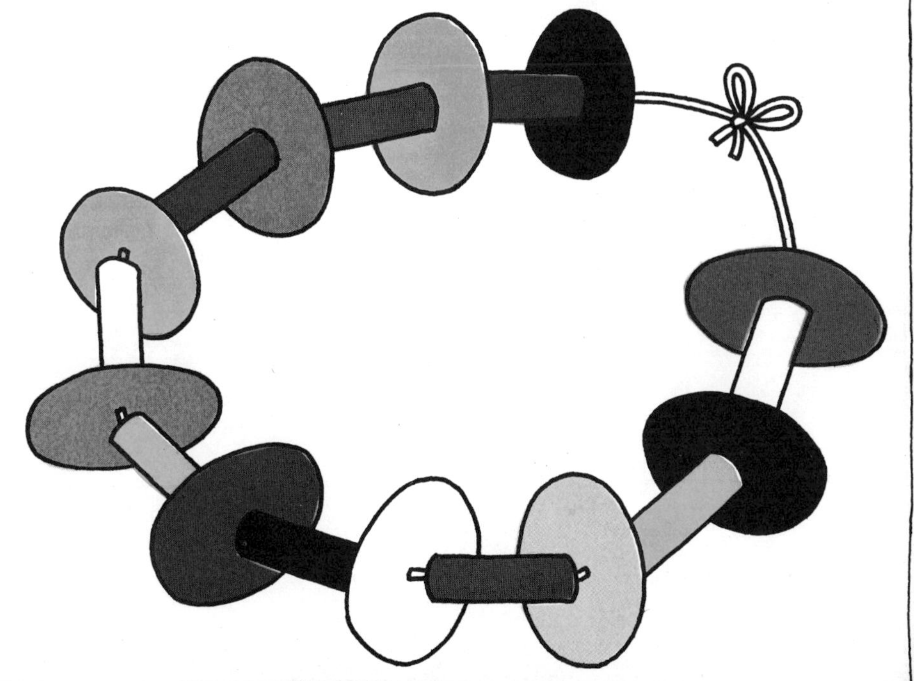

WHATEVER COULD IT BE?

You'll strain your brain! You'll wear out your fingers! And you won't be allowed to peek! It's all a part of a new blindfold game of touch. Simply blindfold someone and then choose an object for him to identify. BUT the blindfolded person may use only one finger to touch and feel the object. Try it. Could be harder than it sounds!

PLAY THE TRAIN-AND-TRACK GAME

The object of this game is to move your "train" from a "home-base town" to a "destination town" along a winding and dangerous "track" without an accident. To make the playing board, draw a circle in the top left corner of a sheet of light-colored construction paper. Give this circle, your home-base town, any name you choose and write it near the circle. Now, in the lower right corner, draw another circle, the destination town. Name this town, too. Next, draw a winding line, your track, from one circle to the other as shown in the drawing. A penny will be your train. Place it on the top circle. Now tilt the paper in any way possible to move the train along the track until you reach your destination. If the train slips off the track (derails) you must start again and try for a safe ride. Have a good trip!

A BUGGY MICROSCOPE

To make your own bug microscope with "slides" to view, begin by rolling a tube from a sheet of black construction paper, working from one of the shorter sides. The tube opening should measure approximately one and a half inches in width. Now, as shown in figure 1 on the opposite page, paste or tape the overlapping side of the paper to prevent unrolling. From one end of the tube, cut off a small section about two inches long as indicated by the arrow in figure 1. Then connect the small tube section onto the larger one by pasting on a cardboard strip about a half-inch wide and two inches long as shown in figure 2. A quarter-inch space should be left between the tubes as shown in figure 2. Your microscope is ready, so on to making "bug slides" for a close look!

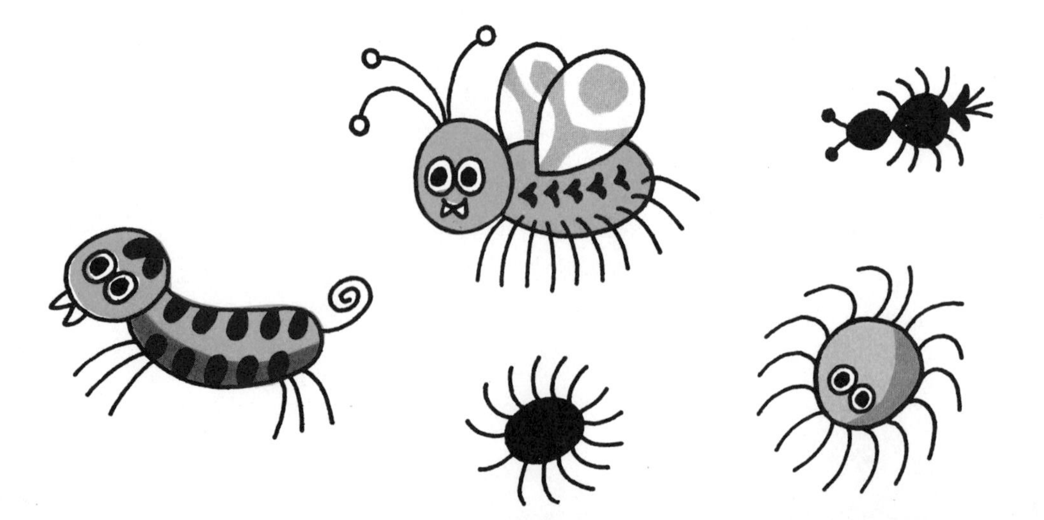

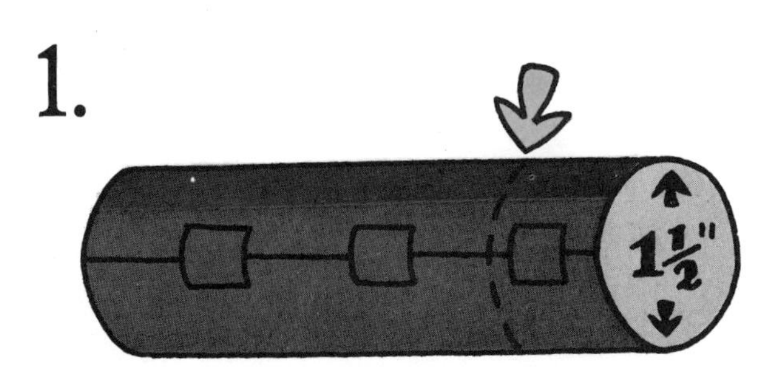

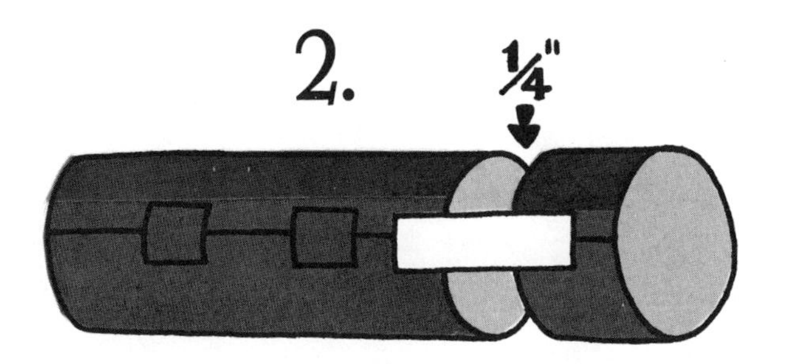

For a collection of bug slides you'll need to make ten or more squares from light bond paper, cut about one and one half inches square. Inventing make-believe bugs or drawing bugs you know about, draw an insect on each slide as shown in figure 3. Now place one slide at a time into your microscope, using the cardboard strip on the bottom as a holder for each slide. Turn toward a bright source of light and watch the bugs fly by!

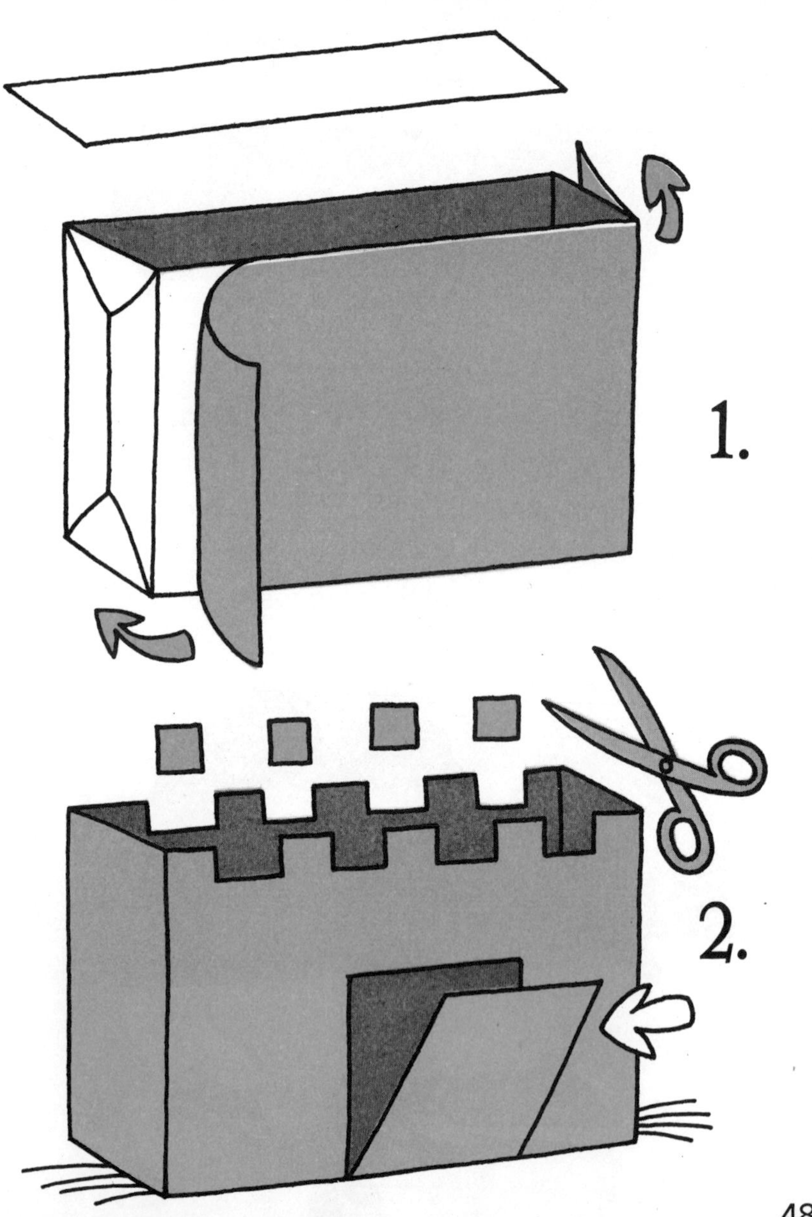

MAKE A CASTLE

You don't have to be a king to own a castle! Just make your own, using an empty cereal box and several other easy-to-gather materials. First of all, tape down the top of the empty cereal box so that it is completely closed. Cover the box with construction paper by pasting it on all sides. Next, cut off one of the long sides of the box, following the example shown in figure 1. This open area is now the top of your castle. To add a touch of medieval design, cut off about four one-inch-square pieces from each side of the castle top as shown in figure 2. A castle door is much larger than the door of a house because it serves as a bridge also, being lowered over the moat (a large pit filled with water, surrounding the castle) when someone wishes to enter. So, to cut your castle door, cut out a three-inch square on **three** sides only as shown in figure 2. Now your castle is ready for two fine towers — so on to the next page!

To make a castle tower, roll up a piece of 9″ x 12″ construction paper the long way, leaving an opening of about two and a half inches, as shown in figure 3. Secure the sides with tape or paste to prevent unrolling of the tube shape. Next, make a tower top by cutting a circle from construction paper, measuring about five inches in diameter. Then, cut out a quarter of the circle as shown in figure 4. Bring the straight edges together, slightly overlapping one edge so that you can secure the cone shape with paste or tape. Now clip off the very tip of the cone, just enough for a straw to fit into. Next, paste a small triangle (cut from construction paper) onto the end of a straw, making a flag and pole. Color the flag if you wish. Insert the straw halfway into the cone and tape it as shown in figure 5.

Now you're ready to make another tower just like this one, and they both should look something like the drawing on the right. Turn the page for the completion of your royal castle.

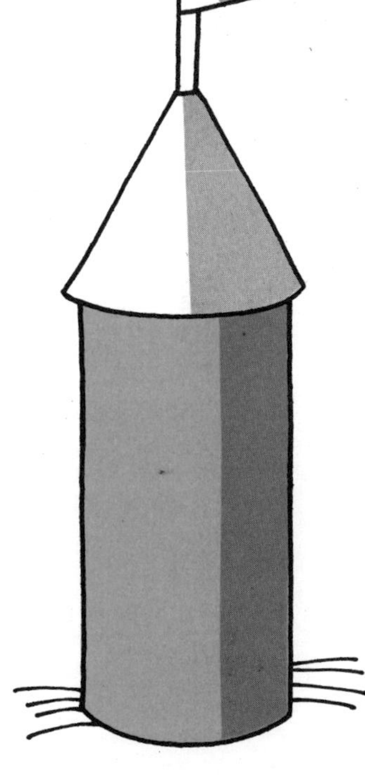

3.

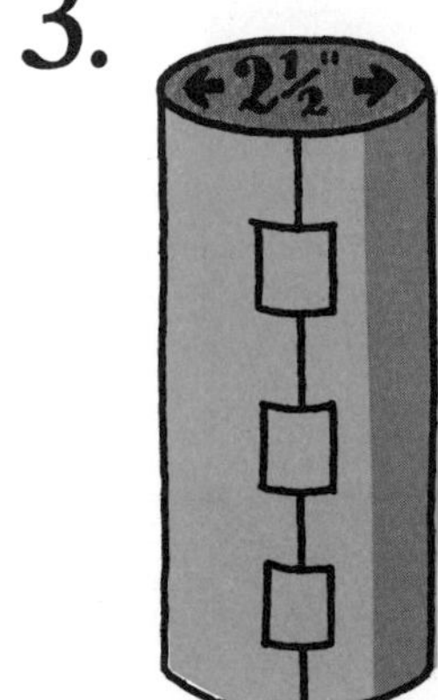

4.

5.

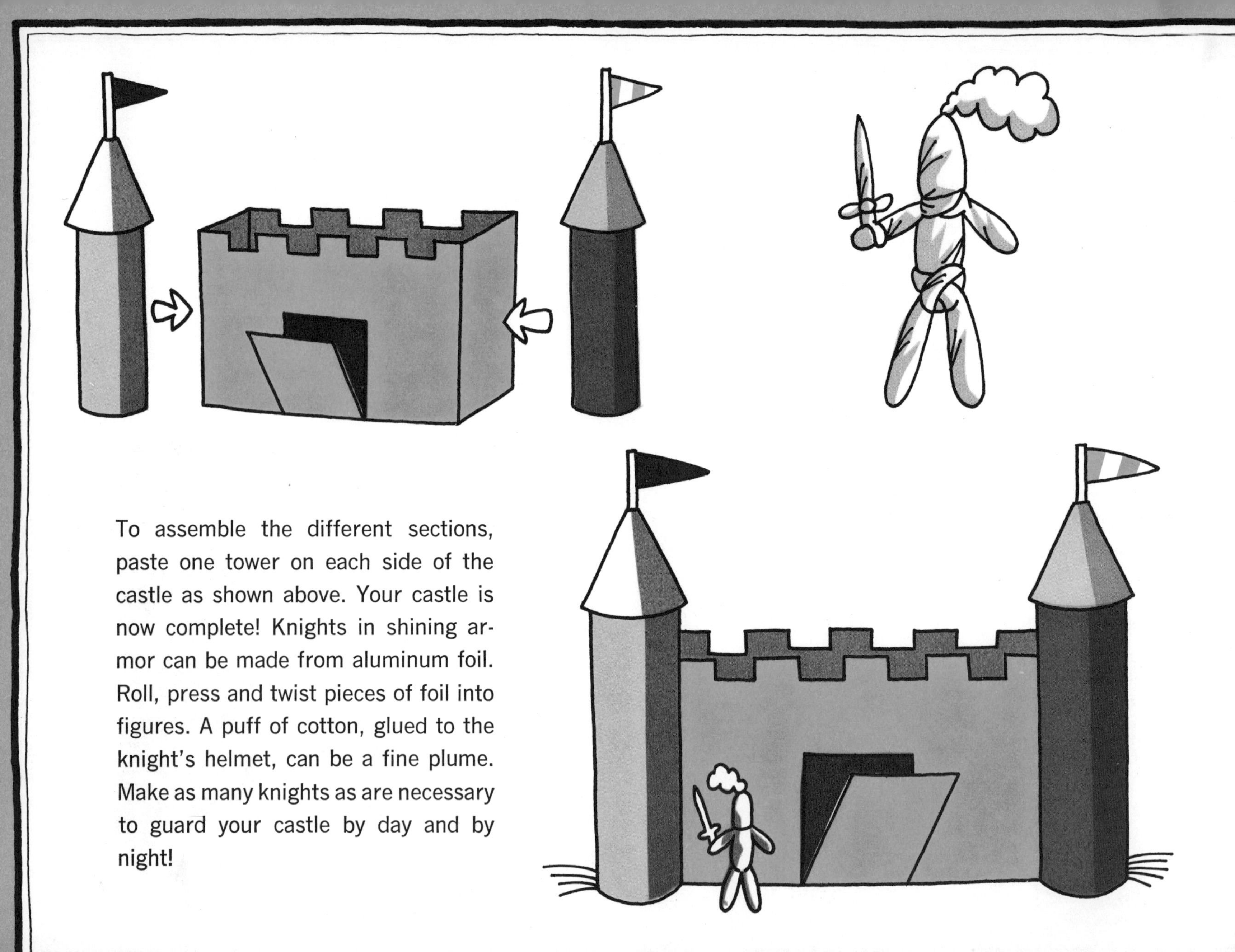

To assemble the different sections, paste one tower on each side of the castle as shown above. Your castle is now complete! Knights in shining armor can be made from aluminum foil. Roll, press and twist pieces of foil into figures. A puff of cotton, glued to the knight's helmet, can be a fine plume. Make as many knights as are necessary to guard your castle by day and by night!

DRAW A SHADOW PROFILE

The most important part of this activity is finding a wall where a shadow can be cast. Sunlight streaming onto a wall can make it possible—or a light thrown upon a wall. Anything between the light and the wall will cast a shadow. When you've found the right spot, tape a large sheet of white paper on the wall. Next, have someone stand close to this paper so that the shadow of his or her profile is cast on the paper. Using a dark crayon, trace the outline of the shadow as is shown with the children below. You'll come out with a real shadow picture! Now have your friends guess whose profile you have drawn.

THE 3-PERSON SILLY-DRAW

1.

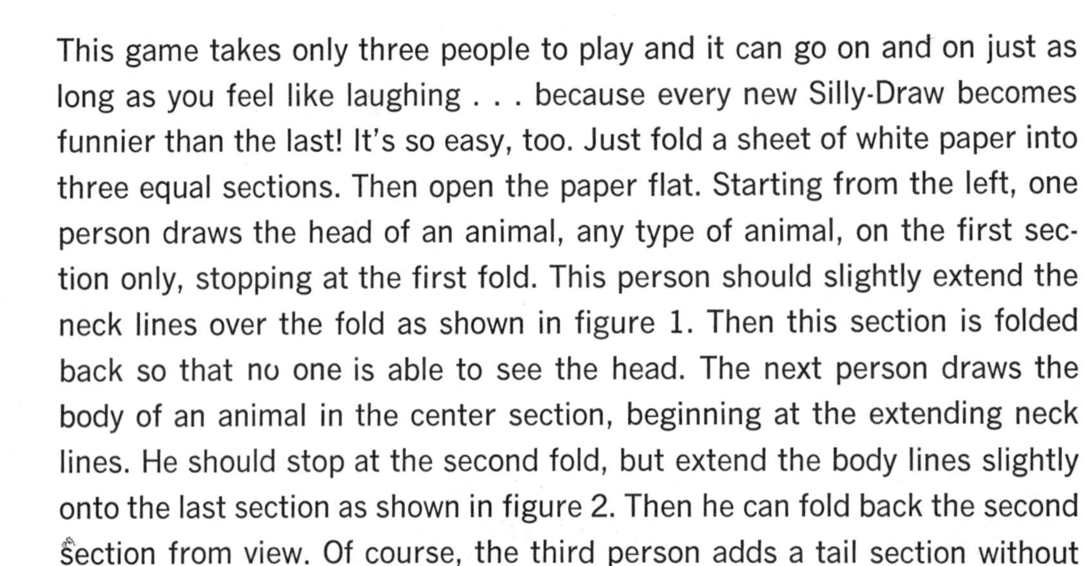

This game takes only three people to play and it can go on and on just as long as you feel like laughing . . . because every new Silly-Draw becomes funnier than the last! It's so easy, too. Just fold a sheet of white paper into three equal sections. Then open the paper flat. Starting from the left, one person draws the head of an animal, any type of animal, on the first section only, stopping at the first fold. This person should slightly extend the neck lines over the fold as shown in figure 1. Then this section is folded back so that no one is able to see the head. The next person draws the body of an animal in the center section, beginning at the extending neck lines. He should stop at the second fold, but extend the body lines slightly onto the last section as shown in figure 2. Then he can fold back the second section from view. Of course, the third person adds a tail section without knowing one thing about the other two sections. What a silly animal will result when the paper is unfolded!

THE ELEPHANT MEMORY

It is said that elephants never forget. Play this memory game to find out how you rate with Mr. Elephant. To do this, group about ten or twelve easy-to-find objects (a teapot, glasses, a piggy bank, gloves, a cereal box . . .) on a table. Then cover these objects with a small blanket or a large towel. Now choose a "guesser" (one who has not seen what is under the cover) to test his memory. Place the guesser in front of the table and lift the blanket, allowing him to look at the objects for about a minute. Then cover the objects and ask the guesser to name each object he saw. For each object remembered, one point is scored. Do this with several or more guessers. The person scoring the most points is winner — he has the elephant memory!

HARK, THE ARK!

You'll need a paper milk carton to build an ark that will really float! Ask help from an adult to cut off the bottom of this container, approximately three inches from the base. This section will be your ark. To make the helm of your ark, tape or paste a straw to one end of the container and bend down the top part of the straw as shown in figure 1. For the roof, cut a rectangle, 2½" x 8", from construction paper. Fold this in half, crosswise. Place the roof onto the ark, slipping each side into the container as shown in figure 1, and taping the roof in place.

But what use is a fine ark without animals to load aboard? And animals are easy to make with pipe cleaners, white or colored. Twist and bend the pipe cleaners, shaping each animal, adding extra pipe cleaners for legs, head, tail, etc. — where and when necessary. Here are some simple figures to follow. When your ark is full of animals, place it in the bathtub or sink and a sea trip may begin!

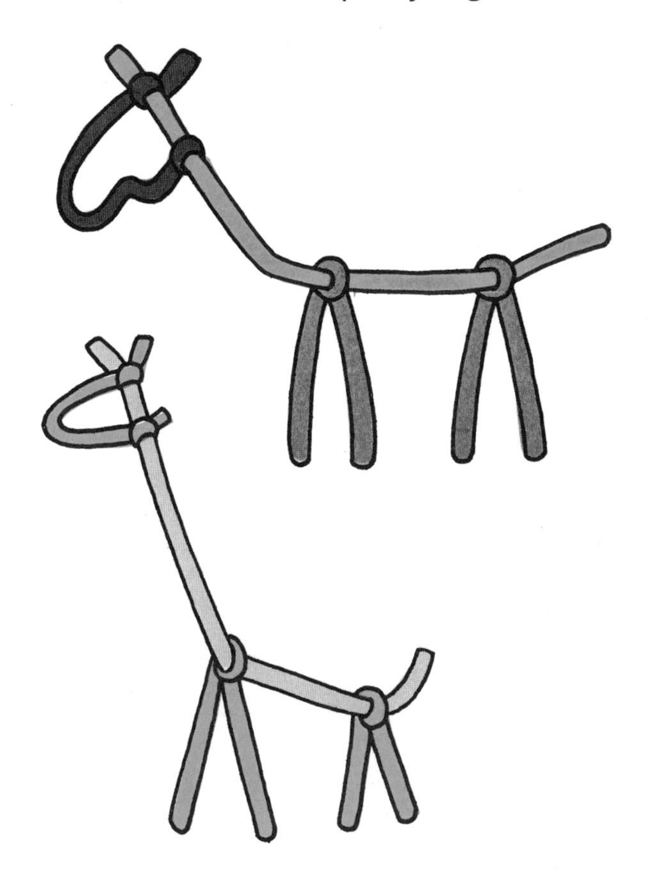

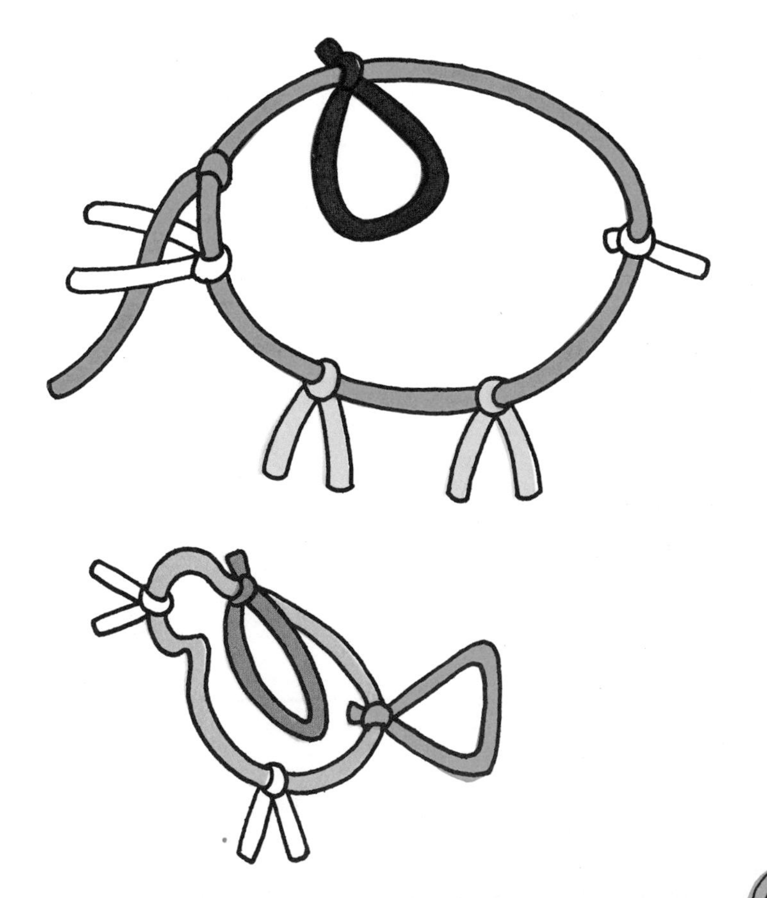

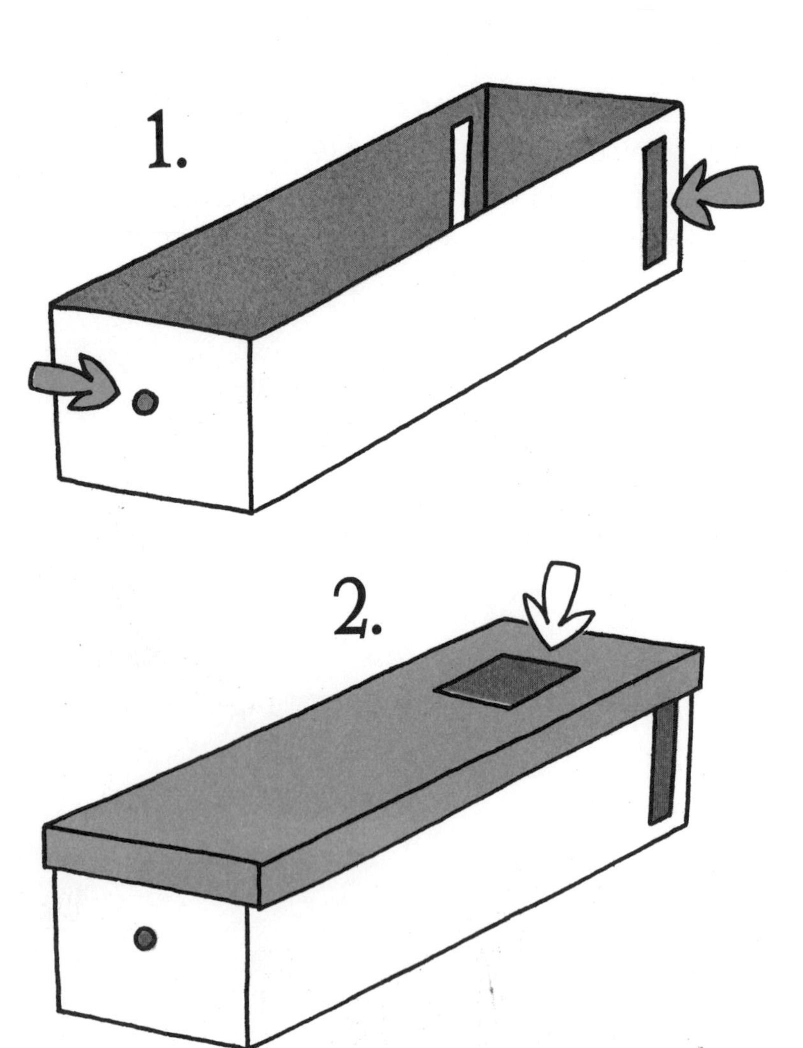

Once you've made your own comic strip viewer, then it's time to put on shows featuring all your comic strip favorites! For the viewer you'll need a shoe box with a top to fit it. First, make a small peephole in the center of one end as shown in figure 1. At the other end of the box, cut a slot on each side approximately an inch from the end and a half-inch from both top and bottom as is shown in figure 1, also. The next step is to cut out a two-inch square from the top of the box approximately two inches from the end as shown in figure 2. The viewer is now complete — so on to the next page for the making of comic strip "films."

HAVE A COMIC STRIP SHOW

From the newspaper or from comic books, cut out the strips of your favorite comics. Now paste these on strips of construction paper to make your film as shown in figure 3. Make a new film strip for each different comic you choose. Be sure that the strips will fit through the slots of the viewer with the top on as shown below. Now for the show! Starting from the beginning frame of a comic film strip, pass the frames into the slots through the viewer so that you can see the whole story by looking into the peephole. On with the show!

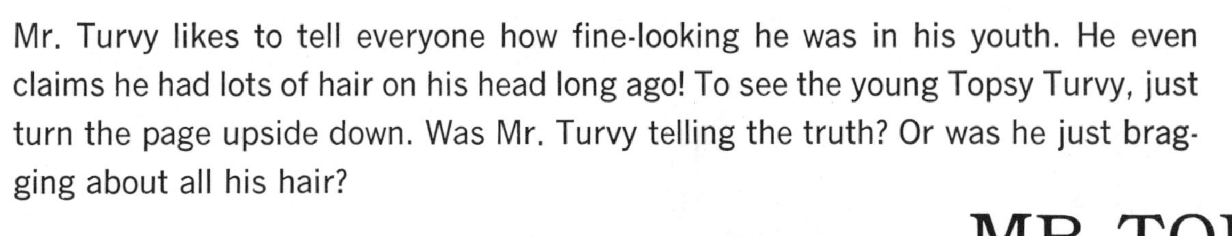
Mr. Turvy likes to tell everyone how fine-looking he was in his youth. He even claims he had lots of hair on his head long ago! To see the young Topsy Turvy, just turn the page upside down. Was Mr. Turvy telling the truth? Or was he just bragging about all his hair?

MR. TOPSY TURVY

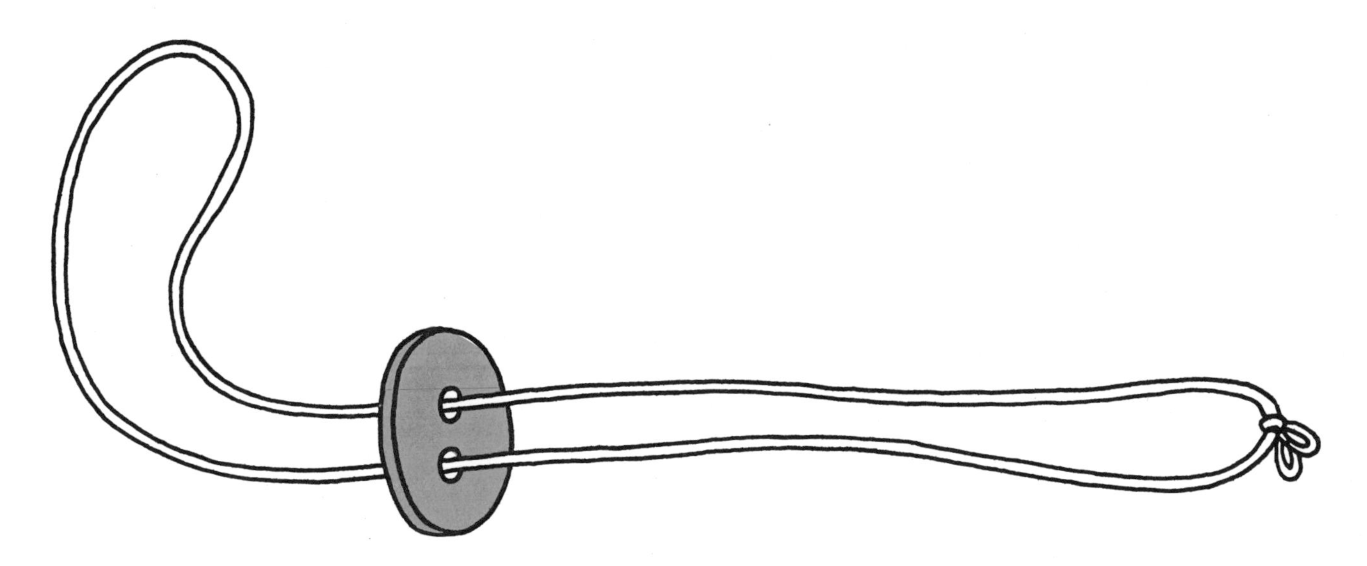

BUTTON FUN

To make Button Fun you'll need only a large button and a piece of string. Just put the string through two holes in the button as shown. Tie the ends securely. Now hold the string with both hands, button in the center. Begin twirling the button, making a wide circle as shown in figure 1. As you twirl with this circular motion, gradually spread your hands farther apart, pulling the string taut as shown in figure 2. The button should spin faster and faster as you tighten the string. Now, loosen the string a bit, making the circle again, then tighten the string again . . . and you have repeated Button Fun! Do it over and over again!

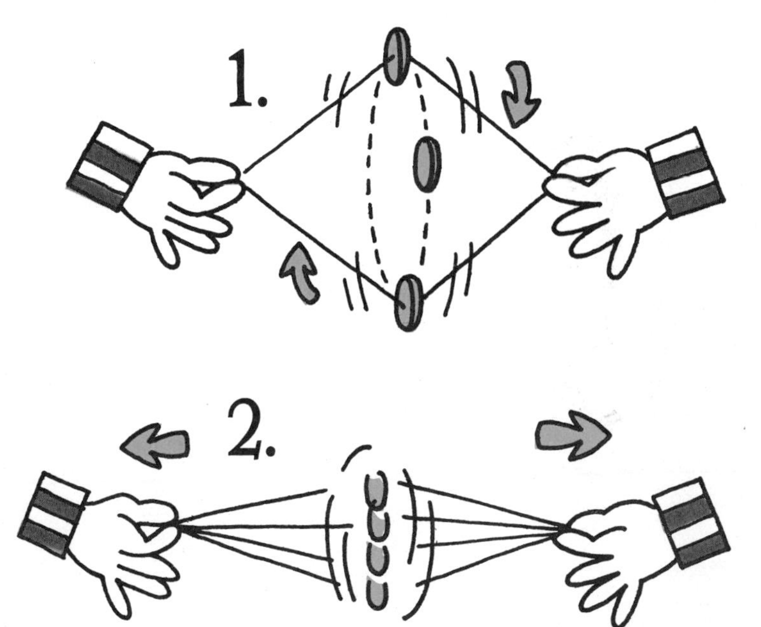

WHERE'S MOUSIE?

Cicero the Cat is certain that a little mouse just ran past him and he's all set for a game of chase. But Mousie is smart. He's suddenly disappeared and Cicero cannot find him. Can you spot the smart Mousie in the picture?

THE NEWSPAPER RING-TOSS GAME

To make your ring game, roll about six sheets of newspaper tightly into a tube. Be sure to roll the long way and to tape the ends together so that the tube does not unroll as in figure 1. Now, using only three sheets of newspaper, follow the same procedure for making a second tube. However, when this second tube is finished, bend it around to form a ring. Tape the ends of the ring together as in figure 2. Next, tie one end of a twelve-inch-long string to the tube and tie the other end to the ring (see below). Holding the tube at the bottom, toss the ring in the air as the girl is doing. The object of the game is to catch the ring with the tube. Try it — and take turns with your friends. Or better yet, help them to make ring games of their own!

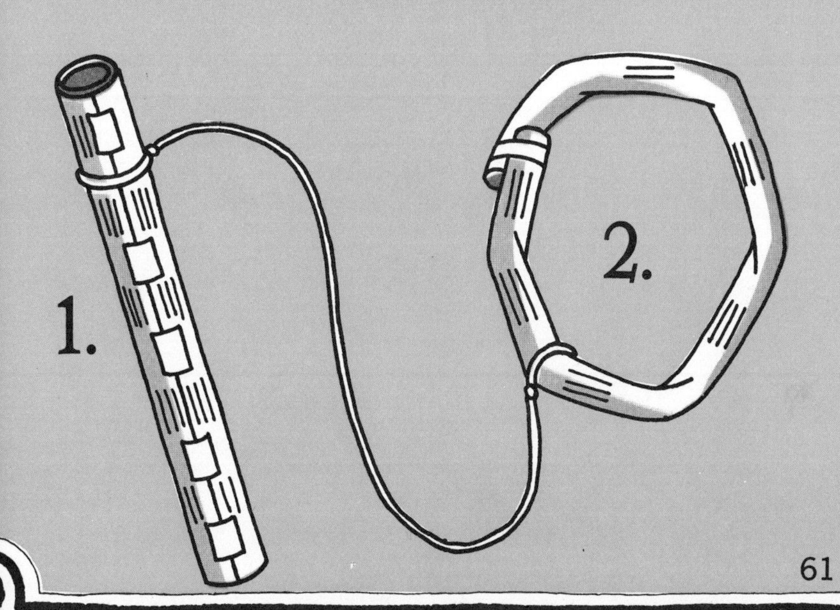